Hello, France!

Tessa Krailing

Nelson

Contents

Goodbye, England

It was almost the end of the summer term.
Mr Belter and the Head Teacher, Mrs Jones, were
taking Rocky's class for a day trip.
They had been on day trips before.
They had been to see how mustard was made and
they had been to a castle.
On this trip they were going a very long way.
They were going on a bus and a boat.
They were going all the way to France!

They set off very early in the morning so that
they would have lots of time to spend in France.
The bus took them to the port where they
would get the ferry boat across the sea to France.

Mr Belter had changed some of their spending
money from pounds to francs.
They could only spend their francs in France.

When they got to the port, everyone got
off the bus.
'Hurry up,' said Mr Belter.
'Everyone get on the ferry boat.'
'It's much bigger than I thought it would be,'
said Rocky.
'Who's going to be sea-sick?' asked Ben.
'Only the boys and girls who eat too much!'
said Mrs Jones.

The ferry boat moved out to sea.
'Goodbye, England!' said Jamila.
'I've never been out of England before,'
said Tony.
The kids watched the port getting smaller and
smaller as the boat moved out to sea.

'I'm hungry,' said Kevin.
'Let's go and find something to eat.'
Kevin bought six chocolate biscuits and two
bags of crisps.
'You might be sea-sick if you eat all that!'
said Ben.
'Rubbish!' said Kevin. 'I'm never sea-sick.'

Hello, France

Soon the boat came into a French port.
'It looks much the same as England,' said Tessa.
'Yes,' said Rocky, 'but they drive on the right,
and listen to the way they are speaking.
That's not like England.'
'Everyone's speaking French,' said Mr Belter.
'I'm glad I wasn't born in France,' said Kevin.
'Why is that?' asked Mr Belter.
'I don't speak a word of French,' said Kevin.
'Stupid boy!' said Mr Belter.
'Now, stay close to me, all of you.
This is a strange country.
If you get lost, come back here to the port and
stand under the clock.'

The kids followed Mr Belter and Mrs Jones into
the French town.
First they stopped at a café for something to eat.
Kevin spent a lot of his francs.
He bought chicken and chips and un ice-cream.
A very big ice-cream.

When everyone had finished eating, Mr Belter said,
'Now, listen everyone. Check your watches.
It's one o'clock now. The ferry boat leaves at
four o'clock, so we have another three hours.
Come with me and stay close.
We'll go and have a look round the town.'

Mr Belter and Mrs Jones took the children
to the market.
There were lots of things to buy.
Kevin saw a big pile of apples.
He was hungry again but he had spent
all his money.
'If I'm careful,' he thought,
'I could take one.
No-one will miss one little apple!'

Silly Kevin picked one of the apples from
the bottom of the pile.
When he took the apple from the bottom,
all the others fell down!

The man who was selling the apples grabbed
Kevin and shouted something in French.
Kevin was frightened.
'It wasn't me who did it,' he said.
'It was those two boys.'

The man didn't speak English but he saw
Kevin pointing at Rocky and Ben.
The man shouted something at the two boys and
tried to grab them but they ran off.
They knew they would never make the man
understand.
The man didn't speak English and
Rocky and Ben didn't speak French.
He saw the boys running off and he began
to chase them.
He shouted again in French but Rocky and
Ben just ran more quickly.

Marc to the rescue

Rocky and Ben were getting out of breath.
They had run out of the market and into
a back street of the town.
They could hear footsteps behind them.
Was the man still chasing them?

Ben looked round.
'It's OK,' he said to Rocky.
'It's not him!'
Rocky and Ben stopped.
They saw a boy running towards them.

He stopped in front of them and began
to speak in French.
'We don't speak French,' said Ben.
'Oh,' said the boy.
'I speak English – a little...
The other boy took the...er...er...'
'Apple,' said Rocky.
'Yes,' said the boy. 'Apple.
Come. I will help you.'

The boy pointed to himself and said, 'Marc.'
Rocky pointed to himself and said, 'Rocky.'
Then he pointed to Ben and said, 'Ben.'
Marc smiled. 'Follow me,' he said.

Around the corner was a horse and cart.
'You. Get in,' said Marc.
'We go,' said Marc, and with Rocky and Ben
in the back, he drove away from the market.
'You're on the wrong side of the road,' said Ben.
'Pardon?' said Marc.
'Over there,' said Ben, pointing to the other side
of the road.
'Ah, no, no!' said Marc. 'Now you are in France,
not in England.'

He drove out of the town, and when he was
a long way away, he stopped.
Marc pointed to a small, white house.
There was a baker's shop next door.
'My house,' he said. 'My mother's shop.
Come. See my mother.'
Ben looked at his watch. It was half-past-one.
'OK,' he said, 'but we have to get back to
the port before four o'clock.'
Marc shook his head. He didn't understand.
Ben pointed to the four on his watch.
'Yes,' said Marc. 'I understand now.'

Rocky and Ben followed Marc into the shop.
'Mother makes bread,' he said.
'She sells in shop here.
I sell vegetables in market, in town.'

Marc's mother smiled at the boys.
She didn't speak any English, so
Marc spoke to her in French.
He told her what had happened in the market and
asked her to show them where she made the bread.

She took them behind the shop to the bakery.
They ate some warm bread with chocolate!
'This is lovely,' said Ben. 'I thought the French
always ate frogs' legs and snails!'
Marc's mother gave them some bread to
take with them.
Marc said it was a present from France.

Time is running out

Rocky and Ben said goodbye to Marc's mother and then left the house.
Rocky looked up at the church clock.
'Hey, look at the time,' he said.
'That clock says twenty-past-three.'
'It can't be,' said Ben.
'My watch says twenty-past-two!'
He asked Marc, 'Is that clock right?'
'The church clock is always right,' said Marc.

'I don't understand it,' said Ben.
'My watch must have stopped.'
'The boat leaves at four o'clock,' said Rocky.
'We've only forty minutes to catch it!'

'My brother's bike. My bike,' said Marc, pointing
to the two bikes outside his house.
'Take the bikes,' he said.
'But we can't bring them back,' said Rocky.
'Leave them at port. Under clock,' said Marc.
'I will get them from there.'

Rocky and Ben got on the bikes.
They would have to ride quickly if
they were going to catch the boat.
'Which way do we go?' asked Rocky.
Marc didn't understand.
'Where's the port?' said Ben pointing
all around.
'Oh,' said Marc. He pointed up the street.
'Turn left at crossroads.'
The two boys began to ride away quickly.
'Remember, ride on the right. The right!' shouted Marc.

Rocky and Ben rode for a few minutes and then came to the crossroads.
'Which way now?' asked Rocky.
'Marc said "left", I think,' said Ben.
'Did he?' asked Rocky. 'I thought he shouted something about going right.
Come on, we have to hurry. This way.'
They turned right.

23

They rode as quickly as they could.
'I'm sure you're wrong,' said Ben.
'I don't remember coming this way.
We should have gone left.
Let's ask someone.'
They stopped a man walking along the road and
asked him the way to the port.
He didn't understand.
He didn't speak English.
Rocky and Ben moved their hands up and down
like the sea.
They made noises like the siren on the boat.
At last the man understood and he pointed
that they should go back the way they had come.
The boys thanked the man and rode away quickly.
'I really think we should learn to speak French
before we come here again,' said Ben.
'Good idea!' said Rocky. 'It'll save a lot
of trouble!'

Will they catch the boat?

Rocky and Ben passed another church with a clock.
'Look at that clock,' said Rocky.
'Quarter-to-four. We only have fifteen minutes.
I hope we're nearly there.'

Just then Ben noticed something was wrong.
'Oh, no!' he said. 'This tyre is flat!
What shall we do?'
'There was a garage back there,' said Rocky.
'Let's see if they can mend it.'

The man at the garage spoke a little English.
He said it would take quite a time to mend
the flat tyre.
Ben told him about the ferry.
'Our teacher will be worried if we miss it.'
The man said he would take them to the port
in his van.

'We have to take the bikes as well,' said Ben.
'Marc asked us to leave them at the port.'
The garage man put the bikes into the back
of the van and then they were on their way.

They reached the port in a few minutes.
'We're too late,' said Ben looking at
the port clock.
'We're five minutes too late!
We've missed the ferry boat and
we can't get back to England!'
'Look!' shouted Rocky. 'The boat's still there!
They must have waited for us.'

They thanked the man from the garage.
They got the bikes from the back of the van,
left them under the clock and
ran over to the boat.
They couldn't see any of the other kids.
'Where is everyone?' said Ben.

Just then Mrs Jones came along.
'Hello, boys,' she said.
'Are the others with you?'
'No,' said Rocky. 'We lost the others so
we came back here.'
'We thought we'd missed the boat,' said Ben.

'But the boat doesn't leave until four o'clock,'
said the Head Teacher.
'But it's ten-past-four now,' said Rocky.
'No, it's only ten-past-three.
Look at my watch.'
Rocky and Ben looked at the Head Teacher's
watch. It said ten-past-three.
Ben looked at his watch.
It said ten-past-three!
Then they looked at the port clock.
'But the clock says ten-past-four,' said Rocky.

'Yes,' said Mrs Jones. 'That's French time.
French time is one hour ahead of English time.
Our watches all say English time, and
the boat leaves at four o'clock English time.
It leaves at five o'clock French time.'
'You mean it's ten-past-four here, but
only ten-past-three back in England?' asked Ben.
'That's right,' said Mrs Jones.
'It's quite simple really.'
'I don't think it's simple,' said Rocky to Ben.
'Well, we haven't missed the boat,' said Ben,
'and we've got time to leave a note for Marc.'
Ben asked Mrs Jones for some paper and a pen and
they went over to where they had left the bikes.
Ben put the note in the basket of Marc's bike.
It said they hoped that Marc would come and
see them in Wellington Square if he ever
came to England.

Soon the other kids came back with Mr Belter.
'What happened to you two?' asked the teacher.
'Oh,' said Rocky. 'We lost you so we came back here.'
He didn't tell Mr Belter how Kevin had got
them into a lot of trouble.
'Well, we're all here now and it's time to get
onto the ferry boat,' said Mrs Jones.

'I like France,' said Rocky.
'But it's different from England.
They drive on a different side of the road.'
'The way they speak is different,' said Tony.
'They have different money,' said Tessa.
'And I'll never forget that their time
is different,' said Ben.
'Their food is different too,' said Jamila.
'I saw lots of different food in the market.
Didn't you, Kevin?'
Kevin didn't want to think about food!
The boat had started to move.
Kevin was turning a funny sort of green colour!
He was feeling very sea-sick!